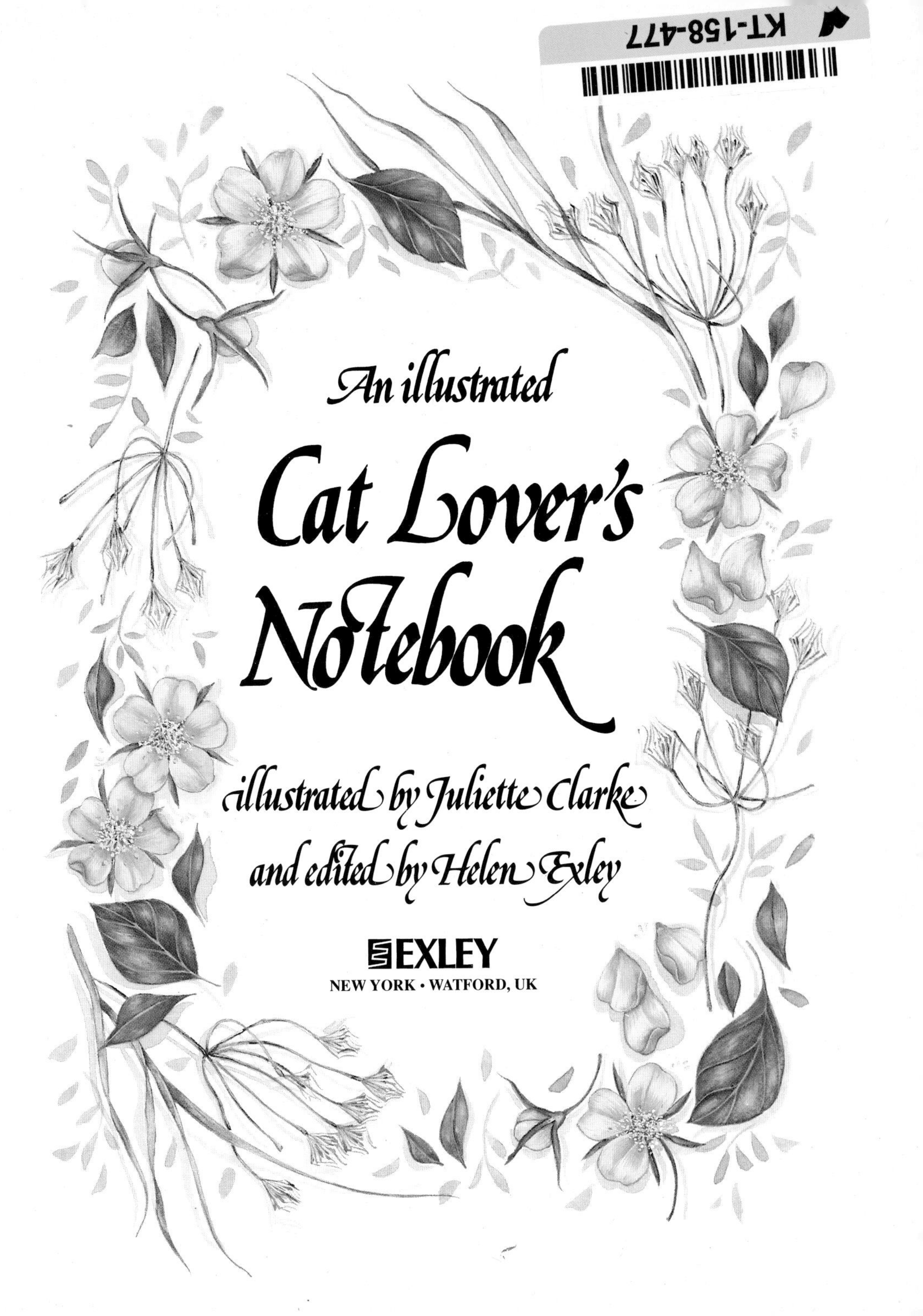

An illustrated

Cat Lover's Notebook

illustrated by Juliette Clarke
and edited by Helen Exley

EXLEY
NEW YORK • WATFORD, UK

A morning kiss, a discreet touch of his nose landing somewhere on the middle of my face. Because his long white whiskers tickled, I began every day laughing.

Janet F. Faure

Other cat books by Exley:
Cat Quotations
Cats a Celebration
The Crazy World of Cats
The Fanatics Guide to Cats
The World's Greatest Cat Cartoons
The Cat Lover's Address Book

Published simultaneously in 1994 by Exley Publications in Great Britain, and Exley Giftbooks in the USA.

12 11 10 9 8 7 6 5 4 3

Edited by Helen Exley.
Illustrated by Juliette Clarke

ISBN 1-85015-454-6

A copy of the CIP data is available from the British Library on request.

Typeset by Delta, Watford.
Printed in Spain by Grafo, S.A. - Bilbao

Exley Publications Ltd, 16 Chalk Hill, Watford, Herts WD1 4BN, UK.
Exley Giftbooks, 232 Madison Avenue, Suite 1206, NY 10016, USA.

Acknowledgements: Celia Haddon: extracts from *The Love of Cats,* published by Headline Books; Celia Haddon & Jess McAree: extract from *Mischief and Delight,* published by Headline Books, 1993; Elizabeth Hamilton, extract from *Cats A Celebration,* published by Charles Scribner's Sons, 1979; Dilys Laing, "Miao", from *In Praise of Cats,* published by Smithmark, 1992; Doris Lessing, extract from *Particularly Cats ... and Rufus,* published by Michael Joseph, 1967; Martyn Lewis, extract from *Cats in the News,* published by Macdonald; Konrad Lorenz: extract from *The Love of Cats,* published by Headline Books; Rosalie Moore, extract from *"Catalogue".* Reprinted by permission; © 1940, 1968 *The New Yorker* magazine, Inc.; Desmond Morris: extract from *Catwatching and Catlore,* published by Arrow Books; Beryl Reid: extracts from *A Passion for Cats,* published by The Cats Protection League, 1987; John Richard Stephens: extract from *The Enchanted Cat,* copyright 1990, Prima Publishing, Roseville, CA, USA; W. B. Yeats: extract from "The Cat and the Moon", published by Faber & Faber.

He lies there, purring and dreaming, shifting his limbs now and then in an ecstasy of cushioned comfort. He seems the incarnation of everything soft and silky and velvety, without a sharp edge in his composition, a dreamer whose philosophy is sleep and let sleep....

Saki (1870-1916)

I put down my book
"The Meaning of Zen"
and see the cat smiling
into her fur
as she delicately combs it
with her rough pink tongue.

"Cat, I would lend you this
book to study
but it appears that you have
already read it."

She looks up and gives me
her full gaze.
"Don't be ridiculous," she purrs.
"I wrote it."

Dilys Laing, "Miao"

Bless their little pointed faces and their big, loyal hearts. If a cat did not put a firm paw down now and then, how could his human remain possessed?

Winifred Carrière

There is some truth in the assertion that the cat, with the exception of a few luxury breeds, such as Angoras, Persians and Siamese, is no domestic animal but a completely wild being. Maintaining its full independence it has taken up its abode in the houses and outhouses of man for the simple reason that there are more mice there than elsewhere.... The appeal of the cat lies in the very fact that she has formed no close bond with [man], that she has the uncompromising independence of a tiger or a leopard while she is hunting in his stables and barns: that she still remains mysterious and remote when she is rubbing herself gently against the legs of her mistress or purring contentedly in front of the fire.

Konrad Lorenz (1903-1989)

A kitten is so flexible she is almost double; the hind parts are equivalent to another kitten with which the forepart plays. She does not discover that her tail belongs to her until you tread on it.

Henry David Thoreau (1817-1862)

Human beings are drawn to cats because they are all we are not – self-contained, elegant in everything they do, relaxed, assured, glad of company, yet still possessing secret lives.

Pam Brown, b.1928

...in moments of calm and happiness, and such moments occur for a cat in a safe and happy home, the full-grown cat will play like a kitten. Even more touchingly, the full-grown cat sometimes becomes a kitten on our laps. Its paws start kneading with the action of a tiny blind baby creature seeking the comfort of its mother's nipple. For there are times when its response to us is that of a kitten – trust, tenderness, simplicity and love.

Celia Haddon and Jess McAree, from "Mischief and Delight"

They taught the children the lesson of the necessity of kindness to smaller, weaker creatures. But mostly they were just there: warm breath, furry lives, acute intelligence, carriers of optimism and faith, for while they seemed never wholly convinced of man's wisdom, they still, with the trust of their lives, gave him the benefit of the doubt.

Nancy Thayer

The love of humans for cats is as strong as the love of humans for other humans. Sometimes stronger. For, despite the gulf between our species, it is a relationship of two equal personalities – if one assumes that human beings are equal to cats, that is. Not all cats do. Some of them make it clear that in their eyes humans are simply charming household pets.

Celia Haddon,
from "The Love of Cats"

Cats, as a class, have never completely got over the snootiness caused by the fact that in Ancient Egypt they were worshipped as Gods.

P. G. Wodehouse
(1881-1975)

The greater cats with golden eyes
Stare out between the bars.
Deserts are there, and different skies,
And night with different stars.

Vita Sackville-West

He was very imperious; very definite and autocratic in his requirements. He really needed a vassal, dedicated to his service alone: to shut and open doors,...find the ping-pong balls he always batted into the most inaccessible places, or carry him on a shoulder.

Marguerite Steen

...cats have a way of endearing themselves to their owners, not just by their "kittenoid" behaviour, which stimulates strong parental feelings, but also by their sheer gracefulness. There is an elegance and a composure about them that captivates the human eye. To the sensitive human being it becomes a privilege to share a room with a cat, exchange its glance, feel its greeting rub, or watch it gently luxuriate itself into a snoozing ball on a soft cushion.

Desmond Morris, b.1928,
from "Catwatching and Catlore"

In these days of tension, human beings can learn a great deal about relaxation from watching a cat, who doesn't just lie down when it is time to rest, but pours his body on the floor and rests in every nerve and muscle.

Murray Robinson

The smallest feline is a masterpiece.
Leonardo da Vinci (1452-1519)

A cat is a pygmy lion who loves mice, hates dogs, and patronizes human beings.

Oliver Herford (1863-1935)

I think that the reason that we admire cats, those of us who do, is their proficiency in one-upmanship. They always seem to come up on top, no matter what they are doing – or pretend to be doing.

Barbara Webster

...you never possess a cat; you are allowed to be in a cat's life, which, of course, is a privilege.

Beryl Reid, b.1920, from "A Passion for Cats"

It is no easy task to win the friendship of a cat. He is a philosopher, sedate, tranquil, a creature of habit, a lover of decency and order. He does not bestow his regard lightly, and, though he may consent to be your companion, he will never be your slave. Even in his most affectionate moods he preserves his freedom, and refuses a servile obedience.

Théophile Gautier (1811-1872)

...when she walked...she stretched out long and thin like a little tiger, and held her head high to look over the grass as if she were threading the jungle.

Sarah Orne Jewett (1849-1909)

The great charm of cats is their rampant egotism, their devil-may-care attitude toward responsibility, their disinclination to earn an honest dollar...cats are disdainful of everything but their own immediate interests....

Robertson Davies, b.1913

...For the cat is a hero for our times - an aristocat ignoring rules, a being which keeps its independence while showing affection, an irrepressible free spirit. In a crowded, regulated and increasingly bureaucratic world, the cat retains a freedom we humans have lost.

Celia Haddon, from "The Love of Cats"

There is little question but that cats are born to the purple. Unlike people, they do not undergo the vulgar period of the nouveau riche but take instantaneously to the luxuries of life with elegant aplomb.

Vivian Cristol

The playful kitten, with its pretty little tigerish gambols, is infinitely more amusing than half the people one is obliged to live with in the world.

Lady Sydney Morgan (1783-1859)

...they [cats] are remarkable animals; they're not like anything else – they're extremely good for anyone who is excitable or who has heart trouble or high blood pressure. If you live with cats, those are non-existent.... They are wonderfully soothing to be with, and they're very very restful.

Beryl Reid, b.1920, from "A Passion for Cats"

A cat is a lion in a jungle of small bushes.
Indian Proverb

It is impossible for a lover of cats to banish these alert and discriminating little friends, who give us just enough of their regard and compliance to make us hunger for more.

Agnes Repplier

Stately, kindly, lordly friend.
Condescend
Here to sit by me, and turn
Glorious eyes that smile and burn,
Golden eyes, love's lustrous meed,
On the golden page I read.

All your wondrous wealth of hair,
Dark and fair,
Silken-shaggy, soft and bright
As the clouds and beams of night,
Pays my reverent hand's caress
Back with friendlier gentleness....
Algernon Charles Swinburne, (1837-1909),
from "To A Cat"

As all cat-loving families have found, cats are indeed catalysts – mellowing human moods, perceptibly changing the impression and atmosphere of any room they have chosen to inhabit. They contribute immeasurably to the lives of countless people, to whom they are friends and confidants.

Martyn Lewis, from "Cats in the News"

Cats fill in all the empty spaces in the human world. The comfortable ones.

Marion C. Garretty, b.1917

One small cat changes coming home to an empty house to coming home.

Pam Brown, b.1928

Oh, cat; I'd say, or pray: be-oooootiful cat! Delicious cat! Exquisite cat! Satiny cat! Cat like a soft owl, cat with paws like moths, jewelled cat, miraculous cat! Cat, cat, cat, cat.

Doris Lessing, b.1919,
from "Particularly Cats...and Rufus"

You can't look at a
sleeping cat and
feel tense.
Jane Pauley

The cat keeps his side of the bargain...He will kill mice, and he will be kind to babies when he is in the house, just so long as they do not pull his tail too hard. But when he has done that, and between times, and when the moon gets up and night comes, he is the Cat that walks by himself, and all places are alike to him. Then he goes out to the Wet Wild Woods or up on the Wet Wild Trees or on the Wet Wild Roofs, waving his wild tail and walking by his wild lone.

Rudyard Kipling (1865-1936), from "Just So Stories"

...anyone who goes through the years indifferent to the beauty, the elegance, the ingenuity, the intelligence, the affection of which the cat is capable - such a person is as impoverished as one who, while walking along a country lane in summer, is blind to the flowers in the hedgerow, deaf to the song of birds, the hum of insects, the whisper of leaves in the wind.

Elizabeth Hamilton, from "Cats A Celebration"

Very few people have the opportunity to know a wild animal as a friend.
Except, that is, for our cats.

Marion C. Garretty, b.1917

It always gives me a shiver when I see a cat seeing what I can't see.

Eleanor Farjeon (1881-1965)

French novelist Colette was a firm cat-lover. When she was in the U.S. she saw a cat sitting in the street. She went over to talk to it and the two of them mewed at each other for a friendly minute. Colette turned to her companion and exclaimed, "Enfin! Quelqu'un qui parle français." (At last! Someone who speaks French!).

Anon

Cats will always lie soft.
Theocritus (c.310-250 B.C.)

The cat went here and there
And the moon spun round like a top,
And the nearest kin of the moon,
The creeping cat, looked up.
Black Minnaloushe stared at the moon,
For, wander and wail as he would,
The pure cold light in the sky
Troubled his animal blood.
Minnaloushe runs in the grass
Lifting his delicate feet.
Do you dance, Minnaloushe, do you dance?
W. B. Yeats, (1865-1939), from "The Cat And The Moon"

A cat does not leap up at you, or lick your face all over or run mad circles round you, making hysterical noises. It meets you at the door and leans very softly against your legs and reverberates.

Pam Brown b.1928

How many cold and lonely midnights have been warmed by the simple presence of this small being, whose affection pervades our solitude?

Carl Van Vechten

Into our artificial lives of ringing alarm clocks, crowded buses and trains, relentless traffic, and busy pavements, cats bring peace. There is no sight so calming as a happy cat asleep; no sound so comforting as a steady purr.

Celia Haddon, from "The Love of Cats"

Cats lack our preconceived notions of what the world is all about. Oblivious to the cares, worries, and desires that plague us, they sit back and watch the world, observing without making judgments, rather like small furry Buddhas. Maybe it's this Zen outlook that attracts us to cats. They accept us as we are, without passing judgment.

John Richard Stephens, from "The Enchanted Cat"

...he is an instrument for the children to learn benevolence upon.

For every house is incomplete without him.

Christopher Smart (1722-1771), from "Jubilate Agno"

Calvin welcomed us with evident pleasure, but showed his satisfaction rather by tranquil happiness than by fuming about. He had the faculty of making us glad to get home.

Charles Dudley Warner (1829-1900)

A cat condenses.
He pulls in his tail to go under bridges,
And himself to go under fences.
Cats fit
In any size box or kit;
And if a large pumpkin grew under one,
He could arch over it.

When everyone else is just ready to go out,
The cat is just ready to come in.
He's not where he's been.
Cats sleep fat and walk thin.

Rosalie Moore, b.1910,
from "Catalogue"

As I look back upon it, Calvin's life seems to me a fortunate one, for it was natural and unforced. He ate when he was hungry, slept when he was sleepy, and enjoyed existence to the very tips of his toes and the end of his expressive and slow-moving tail. He delighted to roam about the garden and stroll among the trees, and to lie on the green grass and luxuriate in all the sweet influences of summer....His conscience never seemed to interfere with his slumbers. In fact, he had good habits and a contented mind. I can see him now walk in at the study door, sit down by my chair, bring his tail artistically about his feet, and look up at me with unspeakable happiness in his handsome face....

Charles Dudley Warner (1829-1900)

...the haughty, the unconquered, the mysterious, the luxurious, the Babylonian, the impersonal, the eternal companion of superiority and art - the type of perfect beauty and the brother of poetry - the bland, grave, competent, and patrician cat.

H.P. Lovecraft (1890-1937)